THIS IS RIDICULOUS! THEY'RE SUPPOSED TO BE FIGHTING WITH *ME,* NOT EACH OTHER!
I'VE GOT TO BREAK THIS UP! NATURALLY, I MUST BE VERY DIPLOMATIC!
AND SINCE THEY'RE UPSET...
...I'LL HANDLE ANY REQUESTS THEY HAVE WITH THE UTMOST OF CARE!
JERRY? TUFFY?
BUZZ OFF!
BUZZ OFF?
YOU HEARD US!
BUZZ!

I'D BETTER STOP THEM FROM FIGHTING!...
...THEY'RE TEN TIMES STRONGER WHEN THEY'RE MAD!
WELL, I'LL JUST HAVE TO TRY AGAIN!
NOW LOOK HERE, JERRY! YOU, TOO, TUFFY!
I'LL HAVE NO MORE OF THIS, DO YOU HEAR?
WE HEAR YOU!
AND DON'T YOU DARE TELL ME TO BUZZ OFF!
OKAY!
BEAT IT!
THAT'S BETTER!

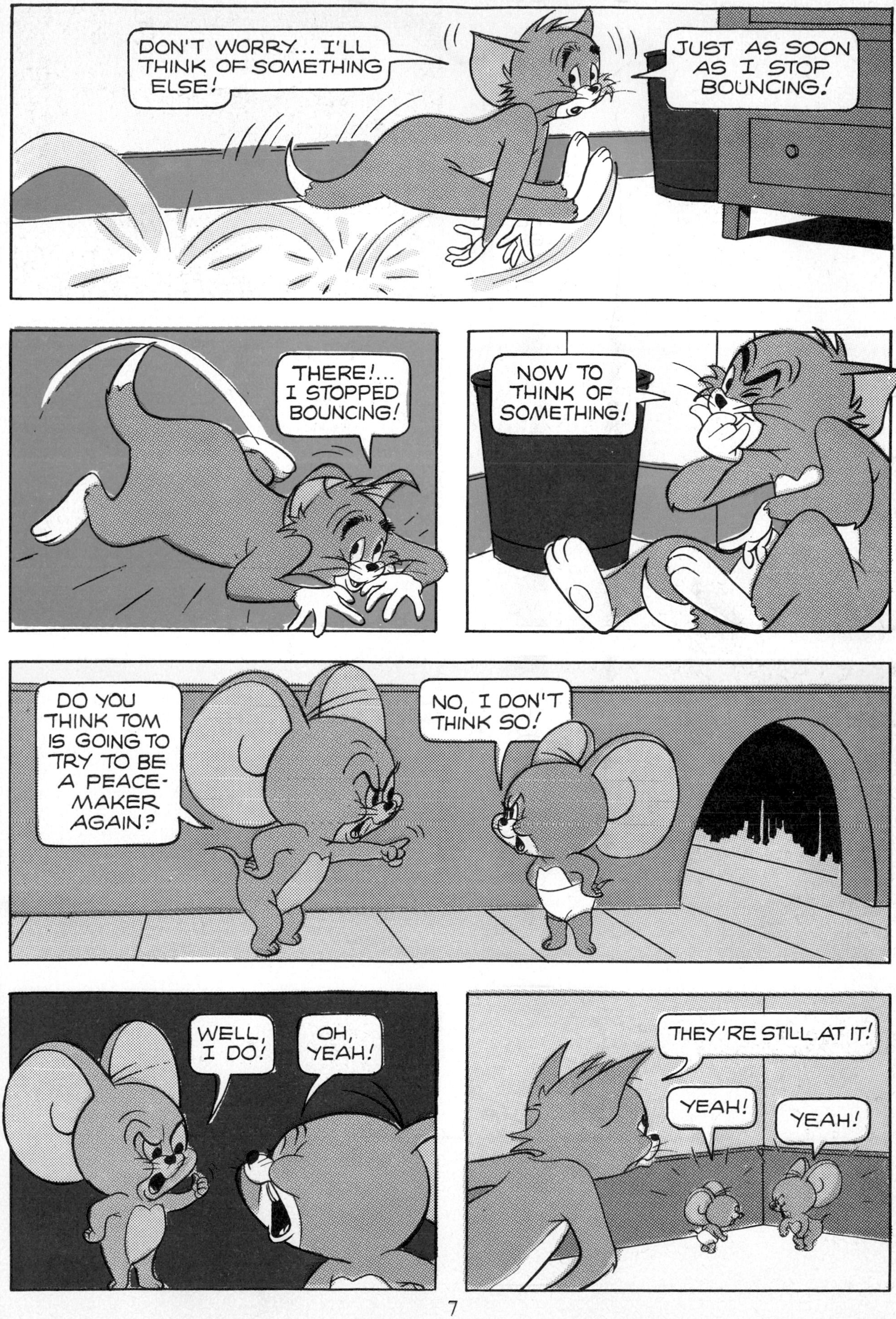
DON'T WORRY... I'LL THINK OF SOMETHING ELSE!
JUST AS SOON AS I STOP BOUNCING!
THERE!... I STOPPED BOUNCING!
NOW TO THINK OF SOMETHING!
DO YOU THINK TOM IS GOING TO TRY TO BE A PEACE-MAKER AGAIN?
NO, I DON'T THINK SO!
WELL, I DO!
OH, YEAH!
THEY'RE STILL AT IT!
YEAH!
YEAH!

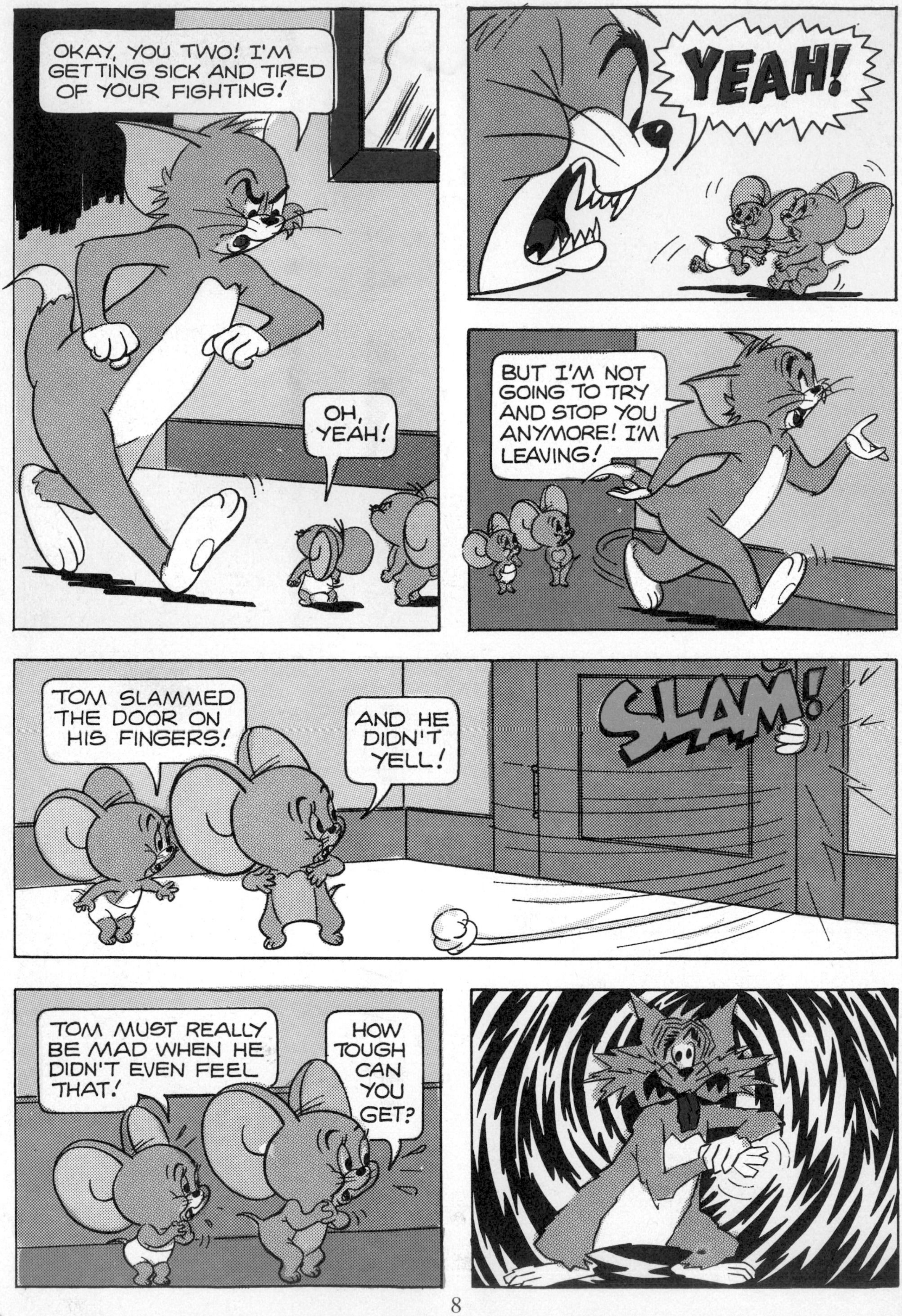
OKAY, YOU TWO! I'M GETTING SICK AND TIRED OF YOUR FIGHTING!
OH, YEAH!
YEAH!
BUT I'M NOT GOING TO TRY AND STOP YOU ANYMORE! I'M LEAVING!
SLAM!
TOM SLAMMED THE DOOR ON HIS FINGERS!
AND HE DIDN'T YELL!
TOM MUST REALLY BE MAD WHEN HE DIDN'T EVEN FEEL THAT!
HOW TOUGH CAN YOU GET?

TOM!
TOM!
GET AWAY FROM ME!
I'M THROUGH TRYING TO GET YOU TWO TO MAKE UP!
HA! HA! HO HO HA HA!
HEY, LISTEN TO THEM LAUGH! I DID IT! THEY'RE FRIENDS AGAIN!
The END

TOM and JERRY
SURPRISE VISIT
IT'S A LETTER FROM UNCLE CLUG! HE'S COMING TO VISIT US!
OH, NO! HE'S THE CLUMSIEST GUY IN THE WORLD!

THE LAST TIME HE WAS HERE, HE BROKE ALMOST EVERYTHING IN THE HOUSE!

HE PROMISES TO BE CAREFUL THIS TIME!

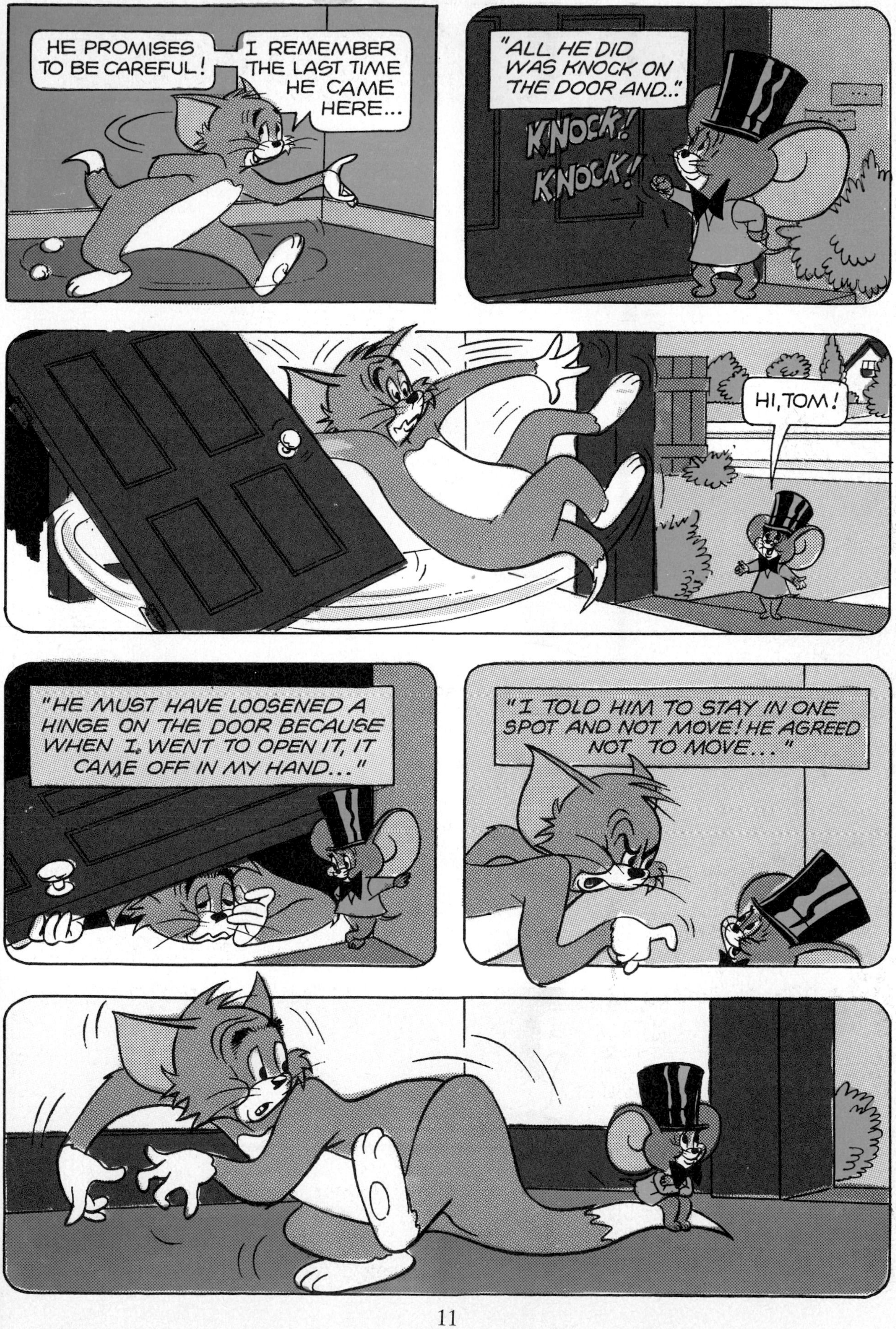
HE PROMISES TO BE CAREFUL!
I REMEMBER THE LAST TIME HE CAME HERE...
"ALL HE DID WAS KNOCK ON THE DOOR AND..."
KNOCK! KNOCK!
HI, TOM!
"HE MUST HAVE LOOSENED A HINGE ON THE DOOR BECAUSE WHEN I WENT TO OPEN IT, IT CAME OFF IN MY HAND..."
"I TOLD HIM TO STAY IN ONE SPOT AND NOT MOVE! HE AGREED NOT TO MOVE..."

IF HE'S COMING AGAIN, I'D BETTER NAIL DOWN EVERY-THING IN THE HOUSE!
WON'T IT BE GREAT TO HAVE UNCLE CLUG VISIT US AGAIN, TOM?
YEAH, IT'LL BE GREAT!
WE HAVE TO GET READY FOR HIS VISIT!
SO DO I!
NAILS

WHAT ARE YOU DOING, TOM?
I'M NAILING DOWN THINGS CLUG COULD TRIP OVER AND PUTTING PILLOWS AROUND TO CATCH THINGS HE'LL KNOCK OVER!
NAILS
BUT, TOM--
NAILS
TOM--
LEAVE ME ALONE! CAN'T YOU SEE I'M BUSY?
SHOULDN'T WE TELL HIM?
WE SHOULD...
...BUT HE WON'T LISTEN!

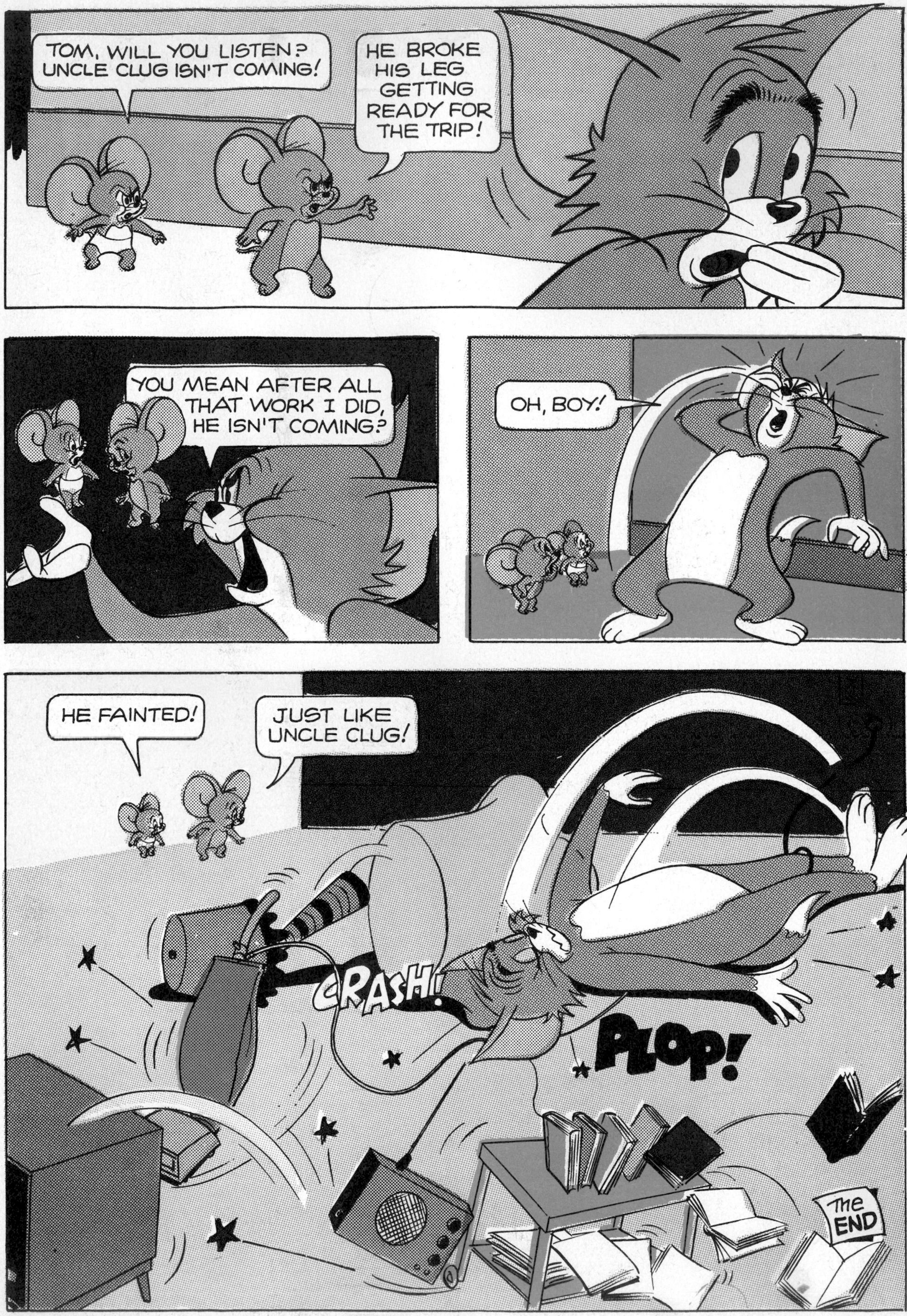
TOM, WILL YOU LISTEN? UNCLE CLUG ISN'T COMING!
HE BROKE HIS LEG GETTING READY FOR THE TRIP!
YOU MEAN AFTER ALL THAT WORK I DID, HE ISN'T COMING?
OH, BOY!
HE FAINTED!
JUST LIKE UNCLE CLUG!
CRASH!
PLOP!
The END

TOM and JERRY
SWITZERLAND, WE ARE HERE!
HOTEL
C'MON YOU TWO! THERE'S THE BUS THAT WILL TAKE US TO THE SWISS CHATEAU RESTAURANT ON TOP OF THE MOUNTAIN!
SHOULDN'T WE WAIT FOR THE NEXT BUS, TOM? THAT ONE'S LOADED DOWN WITH PASSENGERS ALREADY!
NAW!
WHAT DIFFERENCE CAN A COUPLE MORE PASSENGERS MAKE?

AN HOUR LATER...
WHEW! WE'RE LUCKY WE MADE IT ABOARD THIS SECOND BUS, HUH, TOM?
YEAH, BUT THIS ONE IS JUST AS CROWDED AS THE LAST ONE!
AND STILL LATER...
OKAY, EVERYBODY, WE'RE HERE! THAT'S THE SWISS CHATEAU UP THERE!
SWITZERLAND SURE IS A BEAUTIFUL COUNTRY!
JUST REMEMBER ONE THING-- WE'RE NOT HERE TO ENJOY THE MOUNTAIN SCENERY--WE'RE HERE TO WORK!
WELLCOME TO THE SWISS CHATEAU!
SWOOSH
HI, THERE! YOU MUST BE HENRI! I'M TOM!
OH, YES. YOU WROTE TO ME ABOUT A JOB FOR YOU AND YOUR TWO FRIENDS!
OF COURSE, ANYONE WHO WORKS FOR ME MUST BE UPSTANDING!
NO PROBLEM THERE, PAL!
WHAT DO YOU MEAN?
THERE WERE NO SEATS LEFT ON THE BUS!
RIGHT!
WE WERE UP STANDING THE WHOLE TRIP!

HURUMF! ALL RIGHT, YOU CHEESES -- COME WITH ME!
THOSE TWO WILL WORK IN THE KITCHEN! YOU'LL WORK AS AN ICE-SKATING WAITER!
AN ICE-SKATING WAITER?
YOU MEAN I HAVE TO WAIT ON THOSE TABLES WEARING ICE SKATES?
OF COURSE! NOW ALL THREE OF YOU REPORT FOR WORK IMMEDIATELY!
GOSH, TOM, ICE SKATING ON TOP OF THIS MOUNTAIN COULD BE DANGEROUS!
BAH! DO YOU THINK THAT MATTERS TO A LION-HEARTED, VALIANT, FEARLESS AND INDOMITABLE CHARACTER LIKE ME?
THEN YOU'RE NOT FRIGHTENED?
I'M PETRIFIED!

SOON...
WELL, THERE GOES TOM WITH HIS FIRST ORDER, JERRY!
YEAH! KEEP YOUR FINGERS CROSSED!
UH... WHO GETS THIS HOT CHOCOLATE, HENRI?
MR. RICHROCKS! THAT'S HIM SITTING OVER THERE!
GULP! I'VE GOT JUST TWO PROBLEMS NOW...
SQUEEK!
SQUEEEEK!
SQUEEEK!
THE F-FIRST IS GETTING OVER TO MR. RICHROCK'S TABLE!
SQUEEEK!
SQUEEEK!
SQUEEEK!
SQUEEEK!
THEN, IF I SHOULD MAKE IT, THE SECOND PROBLEM IS...
...STOPPING!
SCREEEECH!

AARRG!
PLOP!
PLOP!
OOOOH-!
HMM! I WONDER WHAT BECAME OF THE CUP THAT THE HOT CHOCOLATE WAS IN ?
PLUNK!
AH, THERE IT IS!
OOF!
AND MINUTES LATER...
GOSH, WEREN'T WE LUCKY WE LANDED ON THAT LEDGE ?
GROAN!
NOW YOU JUST SIT YOURSELF DOWN AT ANOTHER TABLE AND I'LL GO GET YOU A FRESH HOT CHOCOLATE!
PANT!
PANT!
PUFF!
PUFF!
A SECOND CUP OF HOT CHOCOLATE FOR MR. RICHROCKS ?
YEAH! AND MAKE IT EXTRA HOT! HE'S GOT SOME COLD LOOKING ICICLES HANGING OFF HIS NOSE!

WELL, HERE I GO AGAIN!
NUTS! I SLIPPED!
SLAM!
HERE'S AN EMPTY TABLE RIGHT HERE, SIR!
SHEESH!
NOW I CAN'T STAND STEADY ENOUGH ON THIS SLIPPERY ICE TO PICK UP MY TRAY!
SQUEEK!
SQUEEK!
SQUEEK!
SQUEEK!
SQUEEK!
I KNOW HOW I'LL DO IT! I'LL BACK UP...
...BEND OVER FOWARD... THEN SKATE OVER AND SCOOP UP THE TRAY!
JUST BE SEATED AND I'LL GET YOU A MENU, SIR!
?
SWOOSH!

SON-OF-A GUN! THAT WACKY CAT DID IT AGAIN!
AARRRG!
PLOP! PLOP!
YUK! YUK! THANK GOODNESS HE GOT SOMEBODY ELSE THIS TIME!
JUST KEEP HOLDING ON TO MY LEG, SIR, WHILE I GRAB ON TO SOMETHING TO PULL US UP!
AH! I FOUND SOMETHING!
HUH?
NO, CAT! NOT THE LEG OF MY —
-CHAIR!
SWOOSH!
AARRG!
AARRG!
PLOP! PLOP! PLOP!
TCH! TCH! I'LL BET HENRI IS GOING TO WONDER WHAT'S HAPPENING TO ALL THOSE HOT CHOCOLATES!

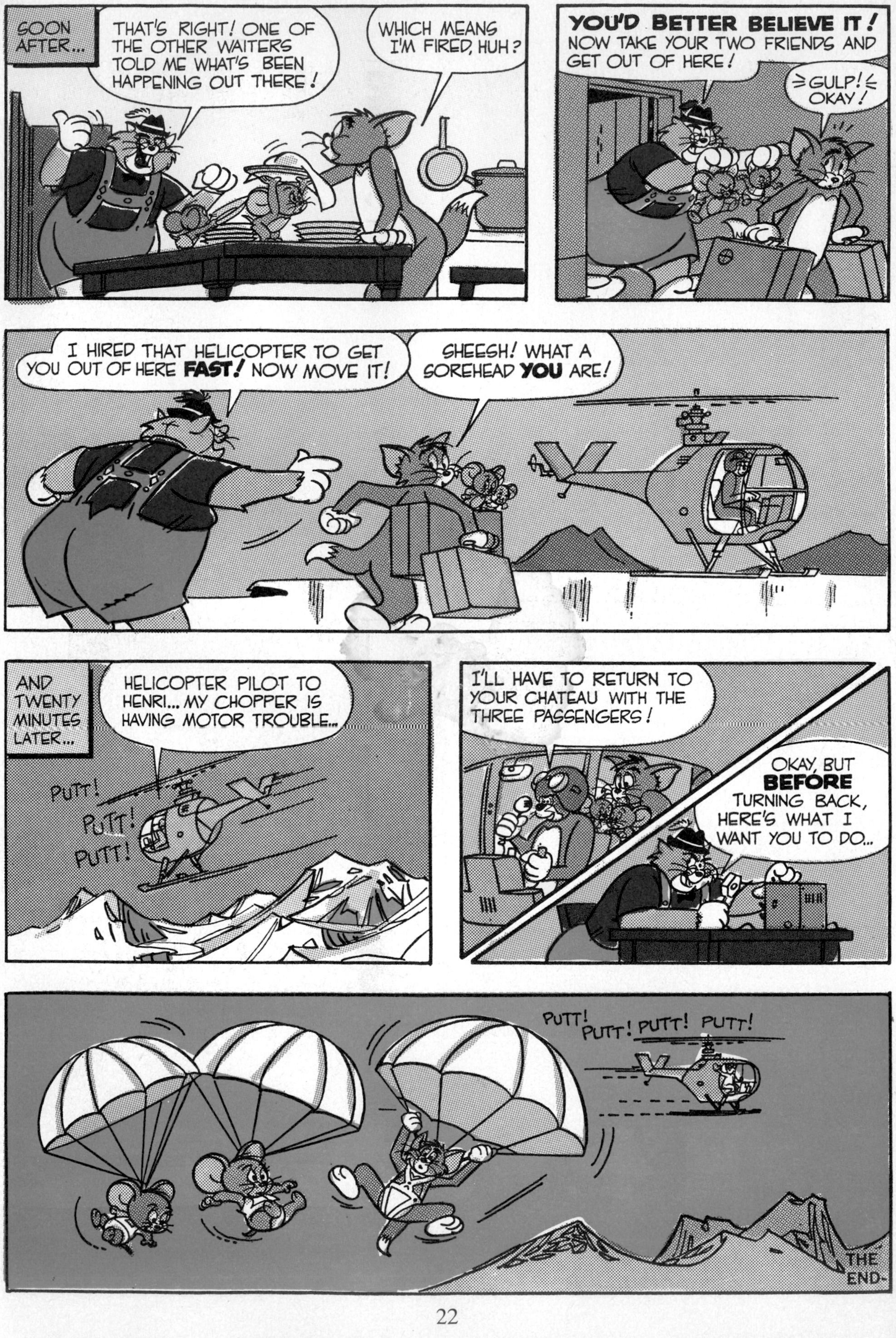
SOON AFTER...
THAT'S RIGHT! ONE OF THE OTHER WAITERS TOLD ME WHAT'S BEEN HAPPENING OUT THERE!
WHICH MEANS I'M FIRED, HUH?
YOU'D BETTER BELIEVE IT! NOW TAKE YOUR TWO FRIENDS AND GET OUT OF HERE!
GULP! OKAY!
I HIRED THAT HELICOPTER TO GET YOU OUT OF HERE FAST! NOW MOVE IT!
SHEESH! WHAT A SOREHEAD YOU ARE!
AND TWENTY MINUTES LATER...
HELICOPTER PILOT TO HENRI... MY CHOPPER IS HAVING MOTOR TROUBLE...
PUTT! PUTT! PUTT!
I'LL HAVE TO RETURN TO YOUR CHATEAU WITH THE THREE PASSENGERS!
OKAY, BUT BEFORE TURNING BACK, HERE'S WHAT I WANT YOU TO DO...
PUTT! PUTT! PUTT! PUTT!
THE END

TOM and JERRY
DOORS WITH FLAWS
QUICK, JERRY, OPEN THE DOOR! "TERRY THE TERROR" WANTS TO PUNCH ME IN THE JAW!
GRRR
OKAY, CLOSE IT! FAST!
SLAM!
HEH, HEH, HEH! I'D LIKE TO SEE TERRY THE TERROR FIGURE A WAY HE CAN SOCK ME NOW!
CLICK!
POW!
90058-502
T.+J.#291-7412

SHEESH! HE FIGURED A WAY!
HEY, TOM...
WHAT MADE TERRY THE TERROR MAD AT YOU?
BEATS ME!
MAYBE IT WAS BECAUSE I THREW A ROCK AT A CROOK WHO I SAW STEAL A WOMAN'S PURSE!
BUT WHY WOULD TERRY MIND YOU DOING THAT?
HOW SHOULD I KNOW?
YOU CAN'T THINK OF ANY REASON WHY YOUR THROWING A ROCK AT A CROOK WOULD HAVE GOTTEN TERRY MAD?
NOPE!
UNLESS...
UNLESS IT WAS BECAUSE THE ROCK *MISSED* THE THIEF AND KONKED TERRY ON THE HEAD!

TCH! TCH! TCH!
SOMETHING WORRYING YOU, JERRY?
HAVE YOU THOUGHT WHAT'S GOING TO HAPPEN WHEN TERRY THE TERROR MEETS TOM ON THE STREET?
TOM'S GOING TO GET CLOBBERED --BUT GOOD!
AND WE CAN'T LET THAT HAPPEN, TUFFY! TOM IS OUR FRIEND!
YEAH, BUT WHAT CAN WE—
FLAP! FLAP! FLAP!
HEY, WHAT'S THAT FLAPPING NOISE?
IT'S JUST THAT BIRD FLYING AROUND UP THERE!
FLAP! FLAP! FLAP!
EXCEPT THAT IT ...ISN'T A BIRD...
NO, IT ISN'T... IT'S PROFESSOR LOOSENUTT!
HEY, WAIT A MINUTE --- PROFESSOR LOOSENUTT IS A CAT!
AND CATS AREN'T SUPPOSED TO BE ABLE TO FLY!

SOME TIME LATER...
TOM! TOM!
DON'T BOTHER ME NOW, BOYS..
BAM! BAM!
I'M PUTTING UP A STEEL DOOR THAT NOBODY WILL BE ABLE TO PUT HIS FIST THROUGH!
BUT YOU WON'T NEED A STEEL DOOR!
ALL YOU HAVE TO DO IS DRINK THIS FORMULA WE BOUGHT FROM PROFESSOR LOOSENUTT AND YOU'LL BE ABLE TO FLY!
DID YOU SAY FLY?
GO AHEAD, TOM-- DRINK IT!
I THINK YOU'VE BOTH GONE BANANAS BUT--
GULP! GULP! GULP!
WHEN YOU FINISH, FLAP YOUR ARMS!
THIS ISN'T GOING TO WORK, BOYS -- IT JUST ISN'T GOING TO...
FLAP! FLAP! FLAP! FLAP!
ZOOM!
SON-OF-A-GUN, IT WORKED!

FLAP! FLAP!
TERRY THE TERROR WILL NEVER CATCH YOU NOW, TOM!
FLAP!
YOU CAN FLY AWAY FROM HIM ANY TIME YOU WANT TO!
I CAN ALSO HAVE SOME FUN WITH HIM!
HE'S BEEN PUSHING ME AROUND FOR YEARS...
AND TODAY IS THE DAY I GET EVEN WITH HIM!
HEY, UGLY FACE!
?
SO, IT'S YOU...
MIND IF I BORROW YOUR BRUSH A MINUTE, PAL?
I WANNA PUT SOME COLOR IN TERRY THE TERROR'S LIFE!
SLURP! SLURP! SLURP!
GASP!

THERE! THAT'S A BIG IMPROVEMENT EXCEPT FOR ONE THING....
YOUR NOSE SHOULD BE A LITTLE RED --- BUT LET'S SEE IF I CAN FIX THAT --
THUMP!
THUMP!
THUMP!
THUMP!
THUMP!
THUMP!
PUFF! PUFF!
THERE YOU ARE! NOW LOOK AT YOUR BEAUTIFUL NOSE!
G-R-R-R-R
UH-OH! YOU APPEAR TO BE GETTING ANNOYED WITH ME, TERRY..
PERHAPS I'D BETTER FLY AWAY LIKE A BIRDIE BEFORE YOU BECOME VIOLENT!
FLAP!
FLAP!
FLAP!
FLAP!

OPEN THE DOOR, BOYS!
FLAP!
FLAP!
NOW CLOSE IT -- QUICK!
FLAP!
FLAP!
FLAP!
WHEW! THAT FORMULA WAS JUST BEGINNING TO WEAR OFF!
THUMP!
THUMP!
HOW COME TERRY WAS SO CLOSE BEHIND YOU, TOM?
BECAUSE HE WAS FLYING TOO! YOU DIMWITS DIDN'T KNOW THAT TERRY BOUGHT SOME OF THAT FORMULA FROM THE PROFESSOR JUST LIKE YOU DID!
IT TOOK MY CLEVERNESS TO OUTWIT HIM WITH THIS STEEL DOOR!
THERE'S NO WAY HE CAN SOCK ME NOW!
SOCK!

TOM and JERRY
"TV or NOT TV"
EVEN A FINICKY CAT LIKE MARVIN JUST CAN'T GET ENOUGH OF "YAHOO" CAT FOOD!
SPOILED, FAT CAT! IMAGINE GETTING PAID FOR JUST EATING!
WHAT'S HE GOT THAT I HAVEN'T GOT?
THE JOB, TOM! THE JOB!
CLICK
I KNOW THAT! BUT I'VE GOT LOOKS, PERSONALITY AND CHARM! I CAN DO WHAT HE DOES!
AT LEAST WE KNOW YOU CAN EAT!
I CAN DO MORE THAN THAT! I COULD GIVE THAT COMMERCIAL SINCERITY AND HONESTY!
DO YOU LIKE "YAHOO" CAT FOOD?
CAN'T STAND THE STUFF!
WELL, SO MUCH FOR HONESTY!

BUT WITH MY ACTING ABILITY THEY'D NEVER KNOW!
TOM, IT'S IN COLOR, AND YOU'LL TURN GREEN!
NONSENSE! I'M GOING DOWN TO THE TV STATION AND TRY OUT FOR THE NEXT COMMER-CIAL!
WHAT ABOUT MARVIN? THAT CAT'S GOT IT IN THE BAG!
WELL, I'M GOING TO LET THE CAT OUT OF THE BAG!
WHAT ARE YOU GOING TO DO?
COME ALONG IF YOU WANT TO WATCH!
WHAT'S HE GETTING OUT OF THE CUPBOARD?
MEXICAN HOT SAUCE! A FEW DROPS OF THIS IN MARVIN'S "YAHOO" WHILE THEY'RE FILMING THE COMMERCIAL AND. LOOKOUT!
HOT STUFF
OH, THAT'LL BE A CATASTROPHE!
SOON...
GOOD! NOBODY'S WATCHING! LET'S GO!
TV STUDIO NO ADMITTANCE
QUIET! YAHOO CAT FOOD! TAKE ONE!
THERE'S THAT TUBBY TABBY! STAY HERE! I'M GOING TO SNEAK BE-HIND THAT CURTAIN NEAR THE CAT FOOD!
MARVIN

MARVIN! TIME FOR DINNER!
JUST IN TIME!
IS YOUR CAT TIRED OF THE SAME OLD THING EVERYDAY? SO WAS MARVIN UNTIL...
HE DISCOVERED "YAHOO" CAT FOOD!
CHOMP CHOMP
WOW! LOOK AT MARVIN GO!
HE REALLY GOBBLED IT UP!
HE JUST CAN'T GET ENOUGH!
ENOUGH OF... GASP!
YAHOO!

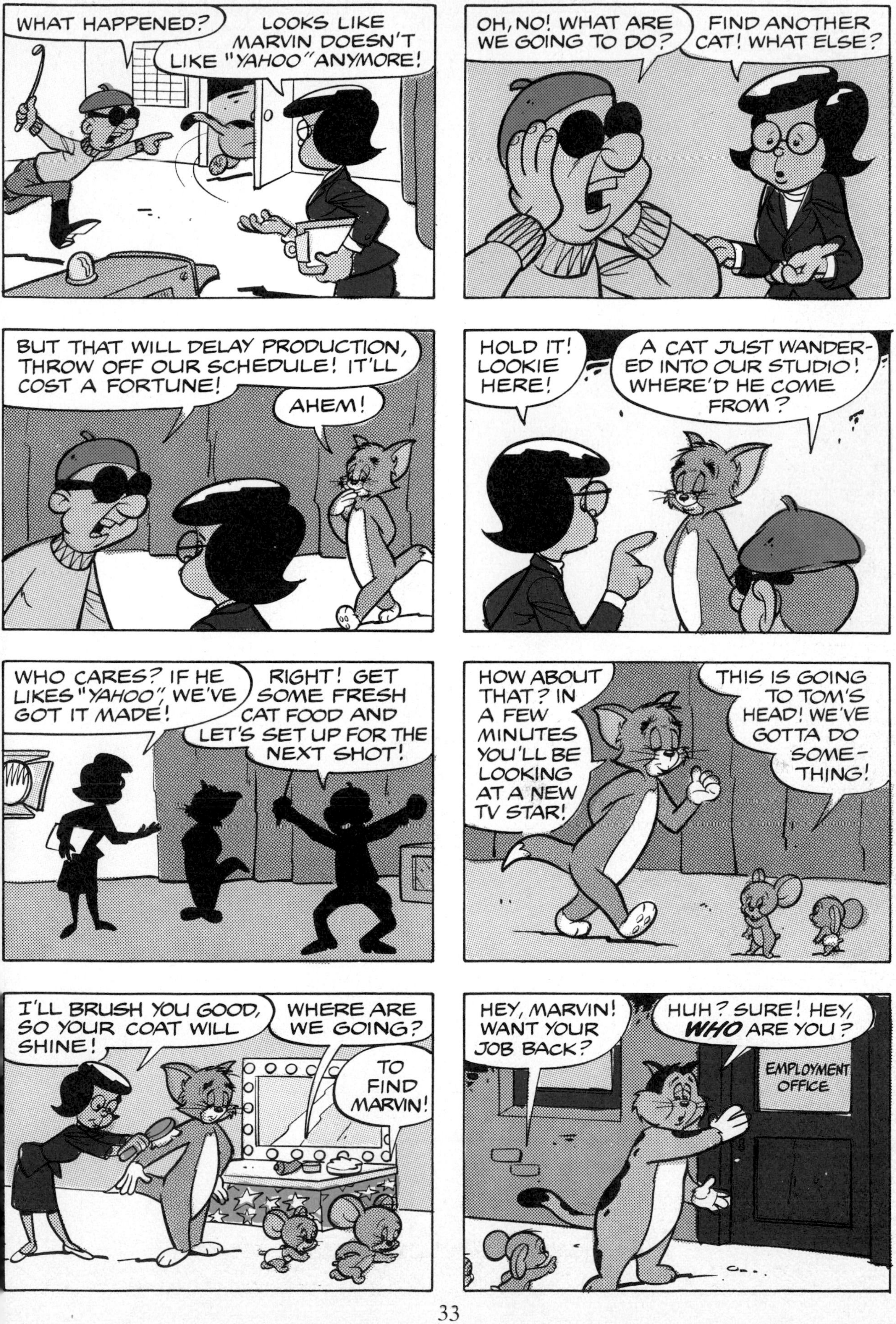
WHAT HAPPENED?
LOOKS LIKE MARVIN DOESN'T LIKE "YAHOO" ANYMORE!
OH, NO! WHAT ARE WE GOING TO DO?
FIND ANOTHER CAT! WHAT ELSE?
BUT THAT WILL DELAY PRODUCTION, THROW OFF OUR SCHEDULE! IT'LL COST A FORTUNE!
AHEM!
HOLD IT! LOOKIE HERE!
A CAT JUST WANDERED INTO OUR STUDIO! WHERE'D HE COME FROM?
WHO CARES? IF HE LIKES "YAHOO", WE'VE GOT IT MADE!
RIGHT! GET SOME FRESH CAT FOOD AND LET'S SET UP FOR THE NEXT SHOT!
HOW ABOUT THAT? IN A FEW MINUTES YOU'LL BE LOOKING AT A NEW TV STAR!
THIS IS GOING TO TOM'S HEAD! WE'VE GOTTA DO SOMETHING!
I'LL BRUSH YOU GOOD, SO YOUR COAT WILL SHINE!
WHERE ARE WE GOING?
TO FIND MARVIN!
HEY, MARVIN! WANT YOUR JOB BACK?
HUH? SURE! HEY, WHO ARE YOU?
EMPLOYMENT OFFICE

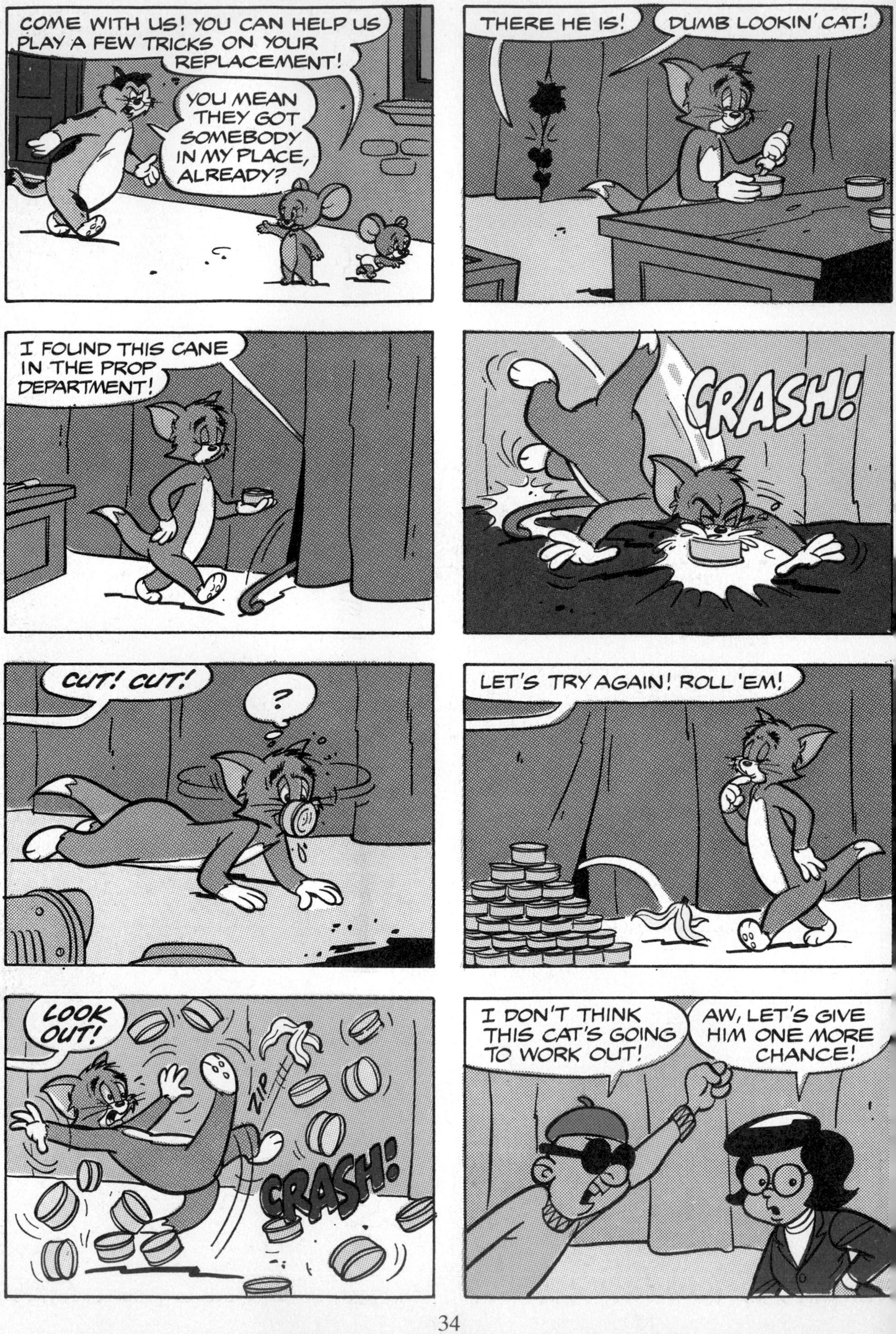

COME WITH US! YOU CAN HELP US PLAY A FEW TRICKS ON YOUR REPLACEMENT!
YOU MEAN THEY GOT SOMEBODY IN MY PLACE, ALREADY?
THERE HE IS!
DUMB LOOKIN' CAT!
I FOUND THIS CANE IN THE PROP DEPARTMENT!
CRASH!
CUT! CUT!
?
LET'S TRY AGAIN! ROLL 'EM!
LOOK OUT!
ZIP
CRASH!
I DON'T THINK THIS CAT'S GOING TO WORK OUT!
AW, LET'S GIVE HIM ONE MORE CHANCE!

HOW DID THAT IDIOT GET MY JOB?
HE PUT MEXICAN HOT SAUCE IN YOUR "YAHOO"!
OH, HE DID, DID HE? WELL, I'LL FIX HIM!
NOTICE HOW TOM LOVES YUMMY "YAHOO"!
HE JUST CAN'T SEEM TO GET ENOUGH... YIKES!
GIMME THAT!
SCAT CAT!
WHAP!
THAT'S GREAT! YAHOO CAT FOOD TASTES SO GOOD, MARVIN FIGHTS FOR IT!
BRILLIANT!
PHOOEY! IF I EVER SEE ANOTHER CAN OF YAHOO, I'LL...
DINNER IS SERVED!
YAHOO CAT FOOD
ZIP
BONK!
YAHOO CAT FOOD
TEE HEE!
The End

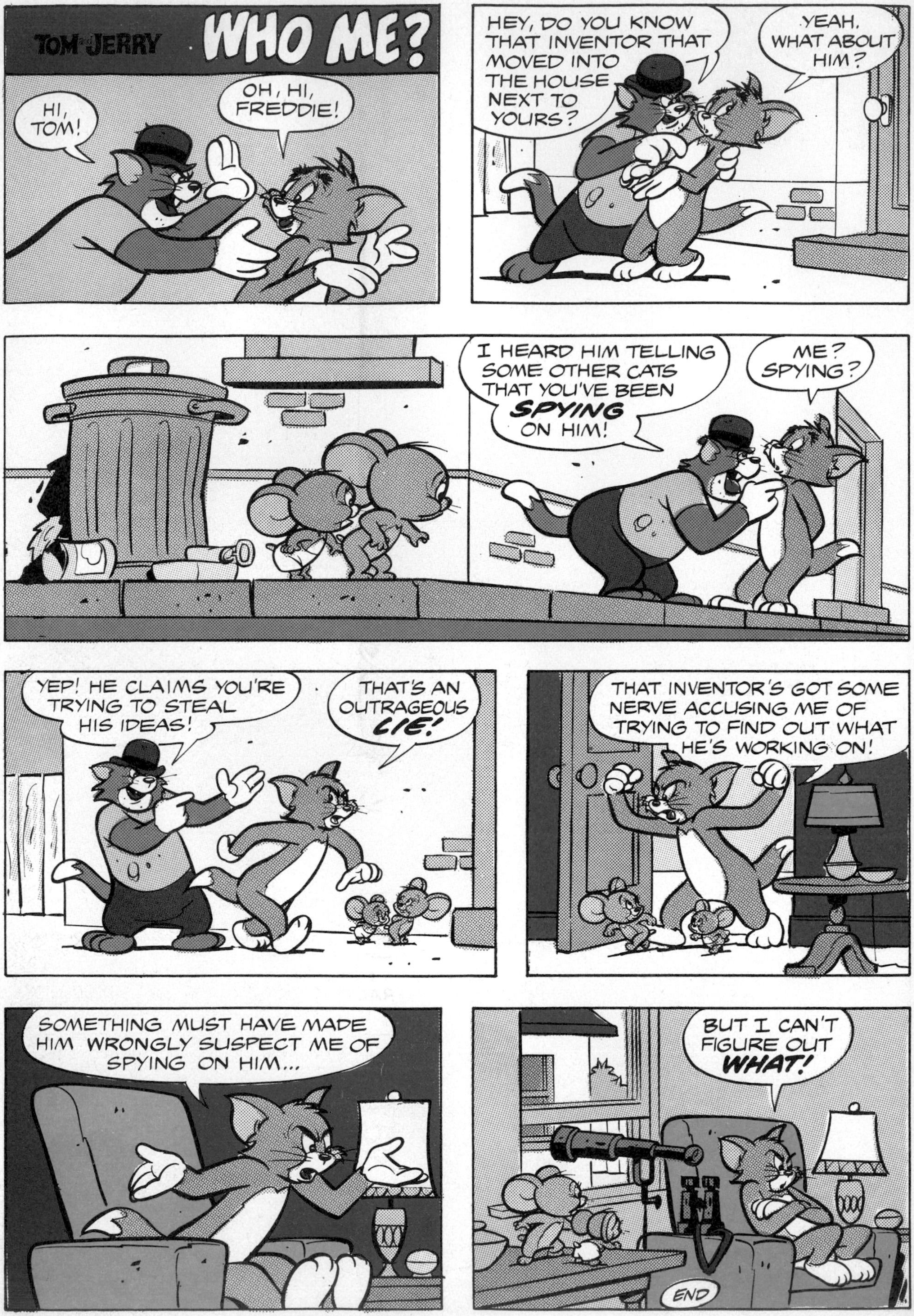
TOM and JERRY
WHO ME?
HI, TOM!
OH, HI, FREDDIE!
HEY, DO YOU KNOW THAT INVENTOR THAT MOVED INTO THE HOUSE NEXT TO YOURS?
YEAH. WHAT ABOUT HIM?
I HEARD HIM TELLING SOME OTHER CATS THAT YOU'VE BEEN SPYING ON HIM!
ME? SPYING?
YEP! HE CLAIMS YOU'RE TRYING TO STEAL HIS IDEAS!
THAT'S AN OUTRAGEOUS LIE!
THAT INVENTOR'S GOT SOME NERVE ACCUSING ME OF TRYING TO FIND OUT WHAT HE'S WORKING ON!
SOMETHING MUST HAVE MADE HIM WRONGLY SUSPECT ME OF SPYING ON HIM...
BUT I CAN'T FIGURE OUT WHAT!
END

TOM and JERRY
OUT TO LAUNCH
GEE, JERRY, THAT SUN FEELS NICE!
CLOSE YOUR EYES, TUFFY! LIE BACK AND ENJOY THE PEACE!
JERRY! THE SUN SURE WENT DOWN FAST! IT'S LIKE NIGHT!
ZIP!
PLOP!
NOW TO TRY ANOTHER PRACTICE THROW FOR THE FRISBEE TOSSING TOURNAMENT!

YOU TWO! WHAT ARE YOU DOING--
WHY DON'T YOU LOOK BEFORE YOU THROW!
IT FLIPPED OVER! THIS IS LIKE A MAGIC CARPET!
I'M AFRAID IT'LL TURN OUT TO BE A TRAGIC CARPET!
YIPE! YOU'RE RIGHT! WE'RE GOING TO HIT THAT CAR!
I WONDER IF THE PAPERS WILL REPORT AN AIR OR CAR ACCIDENT?
WE DIDN'T HIT--
JUST WAIT A LITTLE!
JAMES! YOU AREN'T KEEPING THE CAR CLEAN! WE SEEM TO HAVE-- MICE!
SAFE!
TUFFY, IF WE BOTH ROCK THIS THING TO-GETHER, WE CAN STEER IT!
I HOPE YOU'RE RIGHT OR WE'LL CRASH INTO THAT WALL!
ROCK IT!

IT WORKS! WE MADE IT TURN!
NOW TRY FOR A U-TURN BEFORE THINGS TAKE A TURN FOR THE WORSE!
WE'RE MAKING IT TURN BACK! THIS IS FUN!
SAY THAT-- AFTER WE LAND IN ONE PIECE!
MOMENTS LATER...
WHERE DID MY FRISBEE GO?
ANY QUESTION OF WHERE TO AIM THIS?
CLUNK!
HANG IN THERE, TUFFY!
YEOWW!
MY FRISBEE'S BACK!
SURE, WE STEERED IT BACK-- FOR THE BACK OF YOUR HEAD!
YOU MEAN YOU DELIBERATELY STEERED IT TO HIT ME--GRR!
WAIT! YOU CAN STEER IT, EH? GREAT! WE ARE GOING TO ENTER THE FRISBEE THROWING TOURNAMENT AND WIN!
HOW ARE WE GOING TO ENTER? WE CAN'T THROW A FRISBEE!
WHEN I TOSS THE FRISBEE IN THE CONTEST, YOU TWO WILL RIDE ON IT AND STEER!

NO WAY!
NEVER! I'M TOO YOUNG TO DIE!
DON'T SAY "NO" TILL YOU SEE WHAT THE FIRST PRIZE IS AND REMEMBER--WE THREE WILL SHARE IT!
JERRY, WHAT'S ONE-THIRD OF TEN POUNDS?
ABOUT A MONTH'S SUPPLY!
THIS TEN POUND CHEESE IS FIRST PRIZE IN FREEZY CHEESE FRISBEE CONTEST
WE'RE IN THIS TOGETHER...
AND WE'LL STEER YOUR FRISBEE INTO FIRST PLACE!
AND SO...
SMALLVILLE HIGH SCHOOL STADIUM
FREEZY CHEESE FRISBEE CONTEST
LATER...
JUDGES
LET'S SEE ANYONE BEAT THAT FIGURE EIGHT!
TOO BAD, TOM! I KNOW YOU CAN'T EVEN COUNT TO EIGHT!

JUDGES
HEY! WHAT'S HE USING ON HIS FRISBEE?
MINI-PILOTS! I CHECKED THE RULES!... THE ONLY THING YOUR FRISBEE CAN'T HAVE IS A MOTOR!
LET'S SEE WHAT THE "INTERNATIONAL FRISBEE FAIR PLAY REGULATIONS" SAY! NO... NOTHING AGAINST MINI-PILOTS!
JUDGES
HERE GOES!
HEY!
REFRESHMENTS
SPLASH!
NOW, I ONLY HAVE ONE TOSS LEFT!
TELL US BEFORE YOU THROW IT! AND TELL THEM TO ADD A LITTLE LEMON JUICE TO THE PUNCH! IT'S TOO SWEET!
ONE TOSS LATER...
JUDGES
WE'VE GOT IT ROCKING, JERRY, BUT I--
ULP! SO DO I! I FEEL AIR SICK!

IT'S GOING TO CRASH! THOSE POOR MINI-PILOTS COULD REALLY GET HURT!
YOU BET--ONCE I GET MY PAWS ON THEM!
TO THE STANDS
NO! IT'S STILL FLYING!
GROAN
WOW! THEY'RE DOING A FIGURE EIGHT AROUND THE GOAL POST TWICE! THAT'S A FIGURE SIXTEEN!
HANG ON, TUFFY! WE CAN'T FEEL ANY WORSE!
WANT TO BET? GROAN
MY POOR STOMACH!
MY POOR HEAD!
INCREDIBLE! YOU WIN! NO QUESTION ABOUT IT!
FANTASTIC!
IT'S ALL IN HOW YOU SNAP YOUR WRIST!
MINUTES LATER...
HERE'S YOUR SHARE OF THE FIRST PRIZE! EAT!
EAT? GROAN WHO CAN EAT?
I KNOW I LANDED, BUT WHEN'S MY STOMACH GOING TO LAND?
The END

TOM and JERRY
LUCK WHO'S TALKING
G'MORNING, TOM! LOOK WHAT WE BOUGHT YOU WITH OUR ALLOWANCE MONEY!
A CREAM CAKE!
GO ON AND TASTE IT!
NO THANKS. I DON'T FEEL LIKE HAVING ANY RIGHT NOW!
AW, HAVE A SMALL PIECE, TOM!
NO! YOU HEAR ME? NO!
A-H-H-H-H
A-H-H-H
A-H-H-
CHOOO!
YOU GUYS CAN NEVER TAKE NO FOR AN ANSWER, CAN YOU?

THOSE TWO DUMMIES CAUSE ME NOTHING BUT TROUBLE!
GOSH, TOM, TUFFY COULDN'T HELP SNEEZING WHEN HE DID!
HONK
THE DISASTER TWINS, THAT'S WHAT I OUGHT'A CALL YOU GUYS!
NOTHING GOOD EVER HAPPENS TO ME WHEN YOU TWO ARE AROUND -- ONLY MISHAPS!
AW, YOU'RE JUST GROUCHY BECAUSE YOU DIDN'T GET ENOUGH SLEEP LAST NIGHT!
YOU OUGHT TO GO LIE DOWN SOME-WHERE!
HEY, WHA-?
AAIIIEE!
THUMP!
TOM TOOK YOUR ADVICE, JERRY. HE'S LYING DOWN OUT ON THE FRONT WALK.

AND LATER THAT SAME AFTERNOON . . . .
SUPERMARKET
C'MON, YOU GUYS!
I ONLY TOOK YOU TWO COOKIES SHOPPING WITH ME AS AN *EXPERIMENT!*
IF I RUN INTO ANY TROUBLE GETTING HOME FROM THIS SIMPLE TRIP I'LL *KNOW* YOU'RE BOTH JINXING ME!
THAT'S HIM, CHARLIE!
YOU MEAN THIS IS THE CREEP WHO WINKED AT YOU WHILE YOU WERE STANDING ON THE CORNER WAITING FOR ME?
THAT'S HIM, ALL RIGHT!
NO! WAIT! CHOKE! Y-YOU'VE GOT THE WRONG CREEP, MISTER --- *HONEST!*
POW
BAM
SOCK
HMMM...

CHARLIE...
YES SWEETIE?
THUMP! THUMP! THUMP!
I MADE A MISTAKE! THAT'S THE CREEP WHO WINKED AT ME!
HUH?
SHEESH! I WISH MY SWEETIE WOULD GET HER EYES CHECKED!
WINK
C'MON, TUFFY, LET'S PUT TOM IN OUR CART AND WHEEL HIM HOME!
AND LATER...
HOW IS HE, JERRY?
STILL UNCONSCIOUS...
...BUT I THINK HE'LL BE WAKING UP IN A FEW SECONDS!
YOU MEAN TOM'S GOING TO THINK WE CAUSED HIM THAT BAD LUCK HE HAD TODAY?
WHICH MEANS WE'D BETTER BE WHERE HE CAN'T FIND US
I KIND'A THINK SO!

HEY, WHAT'S GOING ON IN THERE, TOM?
I'M GOING TO SHOOT MY BAD-LUCK FRIENDS, THAT'S WHAT!
HOLD IT, PAL, HOLD IT!
LOOK, YOU CAN'T REALLY BELIEVE THAT JERRY AND TUFFY BRING YOU BAD LUCK, CAN YOU?
YES!
BUT THAT'S NONSENSE! LIKE, IF THEY BRING YOU BAD FORTUNE, THEN THEY SHOULD BRING EVERYONE BAD FORTUNE --EVEN ME, RIGHT?
..UH..I GUESS SO, LENNY!
WELL, THEY'RE STANDING RIGHT OVER THERE AND THEY HAVEN'T JINXED ME!
CRUNCH!
NOW, COME ON, TOM, PUT DOWN THAT RIFLE!
HEY, WHA-?
THAT'S... MY CAR..
?? WHERE'RE YOU GOING, LENNY?
TO GET ANOTHER RIFLE!....
..WE GOTTA FINISH OFF THOSE TWO LITTLE JINXES PRONTO!

TOM and JERRY
(PANT!) SEEMS LIKE I SHOULD BE ABLE TO (PUFF!) NAB THOSE PESTS!
HURRY, JERRY!
(WHEW!) WE JUST MADE IT, TUFFY!
DAGNABIT! MISSED 'EM AGAIN!
WHEN I CAN'T CATCH THOSE MICE, IT GETS ME ALL UPSET!
WISH I COULD FORGET THAT THEY EVER EXISTED AND.... HMM... WHAT'S THIS?
DAILY NEWS
DOCTORS SAY KNITTING MAKES YOU FORGET YOUR CARES AND TROUBLES. IT IS SOOTHING TO THE NERVES....
SOUNDS SILLY, BUT I'LL TRY ANYTHING TO GET MY MIND OFF MICE!
90058-703
T.&J. #292-731

WHY DOES TOM WANT TO CHASE US ALL THE TIME?
IT'S BEYOND ME!
OL' POISON PUZZLES ME MORE EVERY DAY!
HEY, LOOK WHAT HE'S DOING NOW!
WELL!
NOW HE LOOKS AS GENTLE AS A KITTEN!
IT WORKS! I FEEL SO CALM AND CONTENTED ALREADY!
WISH WE COULD UNDERSTAND THAT CHUMP!
MEAN ONE MINUTE AND NICE THE NEXT!
HEY, THERE'S A BOOK ON CATS!
CAT FACTS
LET'S FIND OUT WHAT MAKES TOM TICK!
CATS ARE VERY MYSTERIOUS AND UNPREDICTABLE..
TO UNDERSTAND THE CAT, ONE MUST STUDY THEM VERY CAREFULLY...
HO HUM... AT PEACE WITH THE WORLD!

I'LL SLEEP LIKE A BABY TONIGHT!
HEY, LET'S GO TAKE A LOOK AT THAT PUSSY'S PEEPERS!
ONE OF THE MOST INTERESTING PARTS OF THE CAT ARE HIS EYES. NOTE HOW THEY SHINE IN THE DARK. . .
Z-Z-Z . . .
SHUCKS, HE'S GOT HIS EYES CLOSED!
WE HAVE TO GET A PEEK AT THAT ODDBALL'S EYEBALLS!
I WONDER IF I SHOULD?
OH, WHY NOT?
!
ABOUT HOW MANY CANDLE POWER WOULD YOU SAY THOSE HEADLIGHTS WERE, JERRY?
AW, HE TURNED 'EM OFF!
HEY, DON'T LEAVE US STANDING HERE IN THE DARK!
WHAT GOES ON HERE?
CLICK!
HERE'S SOMETHING INTERESTING!

HIS TONGUE! NOTICE HOW ROUGH IT IS!
MAN, YOU COULD FILE FINGERNAILS ON THAT!
HEY! STOP!
BUT NOTICE HOW SOFT AND NICE KITTY'S PAW IS!
BOY! IT SURE IS COMFORTABLE!!
AND NOTE THE POP-UP FEATURE OF THE CLAWS!
PING!
NOW WATCH THIS!
SEE? THEY'RE RETRACTABLE, TOO!
PLOP!
NOW STAY OFF MY BED OR KITTY MAY SHOW YOU HOW THEY CAN SCRATCH!
GOSH, HOW'RE WE GOING TO STUDY HIM FROM DOWN HERE?
SIMPLE! I'LL SHOW YOU!
I HAVE A FEELING I'M BEING WATCHED!
IT'S A LITTLE TOO DARK TO SEE MUCH!

NOW I'M ON THE BEAM!
LET ME LOOK!
KIDDIESCOPE
THIS DOES IT!
HECK! IT WENT OFF AGAIN!
KIDDIESCOPE
I'M GOING TO TAKE MY KNITTIN' AND GET OUT OF HERE!
NOW HOW'LL WE GO AHEAD WITH OUR STUDY OF THE CAT?
I'LL TAKE SOMETHING ALONG TO READ!
IT WON'T BE EASY, BUT...
TAKE A GOOD LOOK AT ME, BOYS! IT'LL BE A LONG TIME NO SEE!
I'LL TAKE AN APARTMENT!
APARTMENT FOR RENT
THOSE MICE'LL NEVER FIND ME HERE... HMM... WHAT'S THIS...
CAT FACTS ?
CAT FACTS

I'VE GOT THAT BEING WATCHED FEELING AGAIN!
THAT'S FUNNY! THERE'S NOBODY IN THIS ROOM!
THE DOOR'S LOCKED!
GLUE
WE'LL SEE HOW HE REACTS TO A SUDDEN SOUND!
AACK!!
PLOP!
SPLOOP!
WH-WHAT WAS THAT?
HE'S STIFF WITH FEAR!
I C-CAN'T M-MOVE!
OF COURSE NOT! YOU'VE HAD A BAD FRIGHT!
YOUR FEET ARE FROZEN TO THE FLOOR!
YOU?
SEE WHAT I MEAN?
GLUE!

NOTE HOW SLOW KITTY IS WHEN HIS FEET ARE STICKY!
RIGHT!
BUT SEE HOW QUICKLY KITTY CAN WASH HIS FEET!
SLURP! SLURP!
I WANT TO SHOW YOU THE VIEW!
SEE, TEN STORIES STRAIGHT DOWN!
NOW, TRY TO GET OUT OF THAT ROOM!
SLAM!
CLICK!
WE'LL HAVE TO GET OUT OF HERE, IF WE'RE GOING TO CONTINUE OUR CAT STUDY!
IF WE ONLY HAD A ROPE!
HERE'S SOMETHING THAT'LL DO JUST AS WELL!
I THINK IT WAS A NICE THOUGHT LEAVING HIM THAT NOTE!
FAREWELL SAD WORLD WE HAVE DONE JUMPED. JERRY AND TUFFY

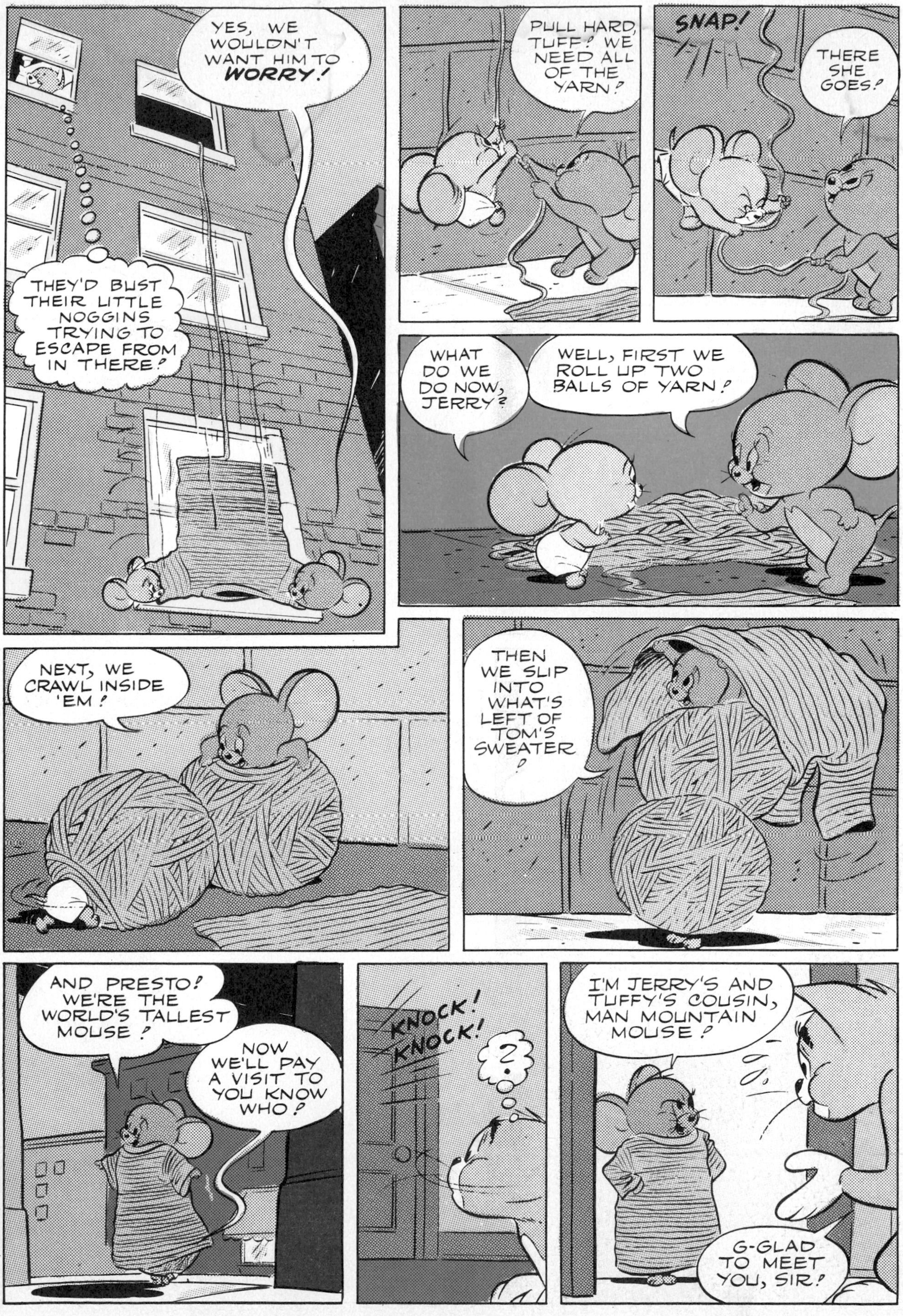
YES, WE WOULDN'T WANT HIM TO WORRY!
THEY'D BUST THEIR LITTLE NOGGINS TRYING TO ESCAPE FROM IN THERE!
PULL HARD, TUFF! WE NEED ALL OF THE YARN!
SNAP!
THERE SHE GOES!
WHAT DO WE DO NOW, JERRY?
WELL, FIRST WE ROLL UP TWO BALLS OF YARN!
NEXT, WE CRAWL INSIDE 'EM!
THEN WE SLIP INTO WHAT'S LEFT OF TOM'S SWEATER!
AND PRESTO! WE'RE THE WORLD'S TALLEST MOUSE!
NOW WE'LL PAY A VISIT TO YOU KNOW WHO!
KNOCK! KNOCK!
?
I'M JERRY'S AND TUFFY'S COUSIN, MAN MOUNTAIN MOUSE!
G-GLAD TO MEET YOU, SIR!

I TRUST YOU ARE TAKING GOOD CARE OF THE LITTLE FELLOWS?
OH, YES, INDEED! COME, I'LL SHOW YOU?
GULP?
HORRORS!
YOU ARE RESPONSIBLE FOR THIS?
I CONFESS?
DO YOU REALIZE WHAT YOU HAVE DONE?
YES?
THINK OF THE SAD FATE OF THOSE POOR INNOCENT LITTLE DARLINGS?
AND YOU'LL SUFFER THE CATSEQUENCES?
OH, I'M SO (SOB?) SORRY?
LATER...
HELLO, THOMAS CAT? THIS IS M.M. MOUSE SPEAKING?
LAY IT ON STRONG, JERRY?
WE BROUGHT POOR JERRY AND TUFFY HOME---YOU'D BETTER COME AT ONCE?

I'LL DO ALL I CAN TO MAKE THEM FEEL BETTER!
MOAN! GROAN!
I'LL EVEN KNIT YOU BED JACKETS!
HOW THOUGHTY OF YOU!
MY KNITTING! IT'S GONE!
WE'VE ALWAYS WANTED BED JACKETS, JACK!
SO!
YOU WON'T MAKE THEM TOO BIG, WILL YOU?
OH, NO, I'LL HAVE YOU TRY THIS ON FOR SIZE!
UH-OH!
NOW DON'T TELL ME WHERE I'VE SEEN YOU... I WANT TO GUESS!
NOW, WOULD MY LITTLE FRIENDS LIKE TO SEE ANOTHER OF PUSSY'S PECULIARITIES?
OH, I SHOULD SAY WE WOULD!
I JUST LOVE BATTING BALLS OF YARN!
CLUNK!

TOM JERRY
SAME OLD THING
OH, WELL, ANOTHER DAY! SAME OLD THING!
JERRY, DID YOU SEE WHAT I SAW?
I SURE DID! AND THAT'S NOT THE SAME OLD THING!
WHAT--

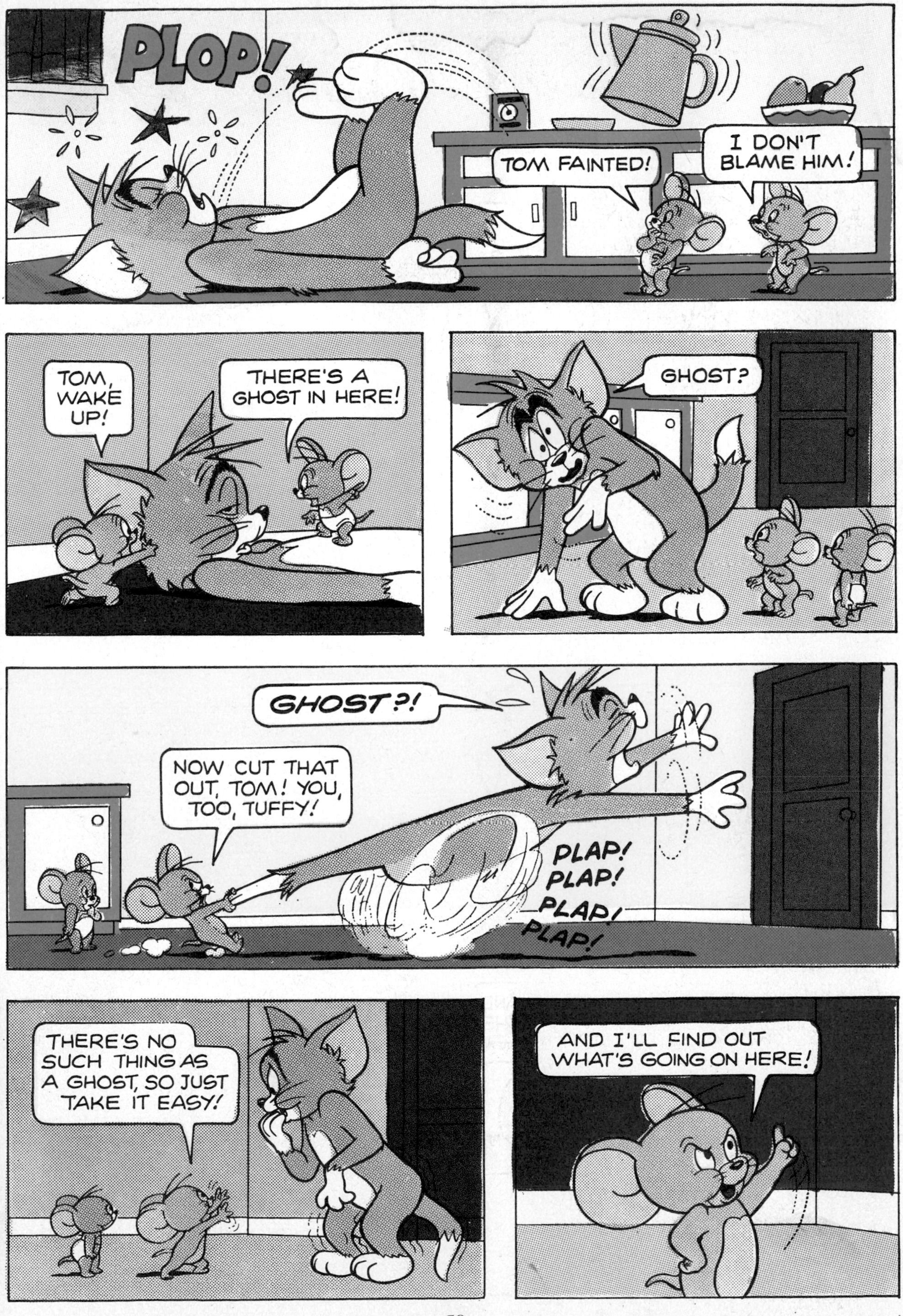
PLOP!
TOM FAINTED!
I DON'T BLAME HIM!
TOM, WAKE UP!
THERE'S A GHOST IN HERE!
GHOST?
GHOST?!
NOW CUT THAT OUT, TOM! YOU, TOO, TUFFY!
PLAP! PLAP! PLAP! PLAP!
THERE'S NO SUCH THING AS A GHOST, SO JUST TAKE IT EASY!
AND I'LL FIND OUT WHAT'S GOING ON HERE!

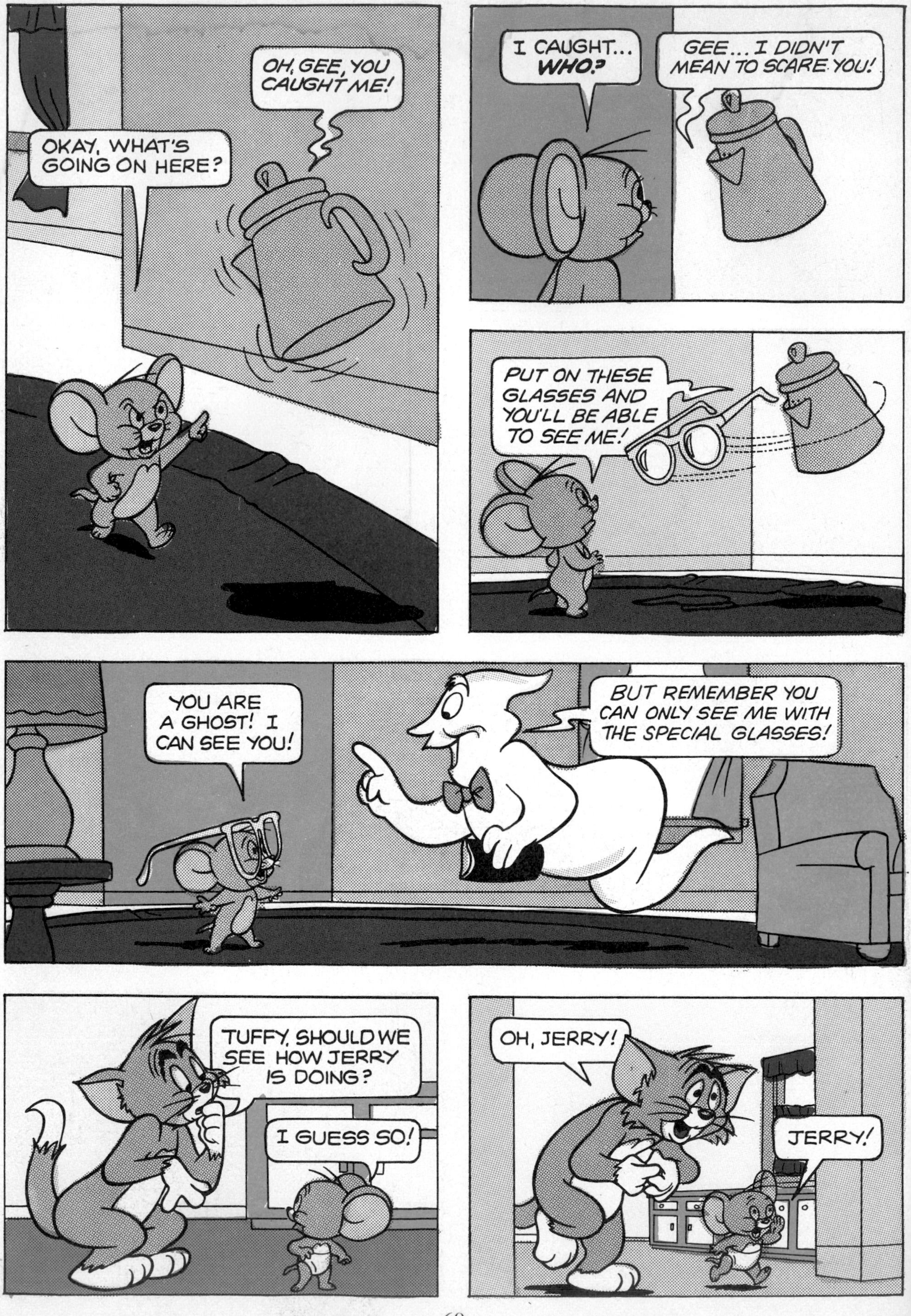
OH, GEE, YOU CAUGHT ME!
OKAY, WHAT'S GOING ON HERE?
I CAUGHT... WHO?
GEE... I DIDN'T MEAN TO SCARE YOU!
PUT ON THESE GLASSES AND YOU'LL BE ABLE TO SEE ME!
YOU ARE A GHOST! I CAN SEE YOU!
BUT REMEMBER YOU CAN ONLY SEE ME WITH THE SPECIAL GLASSES!
TUFFY, SHOULD WE SEE HOW JERRY IS DOING?
I GUESS SO!
OH, JERRY!
JERRY!

HE'S TALKING TO HIMSELF!
WHAT'S THE MATTER WITH JERRY?
I'M NOT TALKING TO MYSELF!
TALK TO THEM SO THEY WON'T THINK I'VE FLIPPED OUT!
I CAN'T! I'M NOT SUPPOSED TO TALK TO STRANGERS!
HONEST, TOM, TUFFY! HE'S A REAL GHOST, BUT HE'S REALLY HARMLESS!
SO ARE YOU, TOO, JERRY!
LET'S GET OUT OF HERE, TUFFY! IT MIGHT BE CATCHING!
DON'T JUST STAND THERE! DO SOMETHING TO LET TOM KNOW YOU'RE REAL!
OKAY! BUT I WON'T TALK TO HIM!
THANKS!
POW!

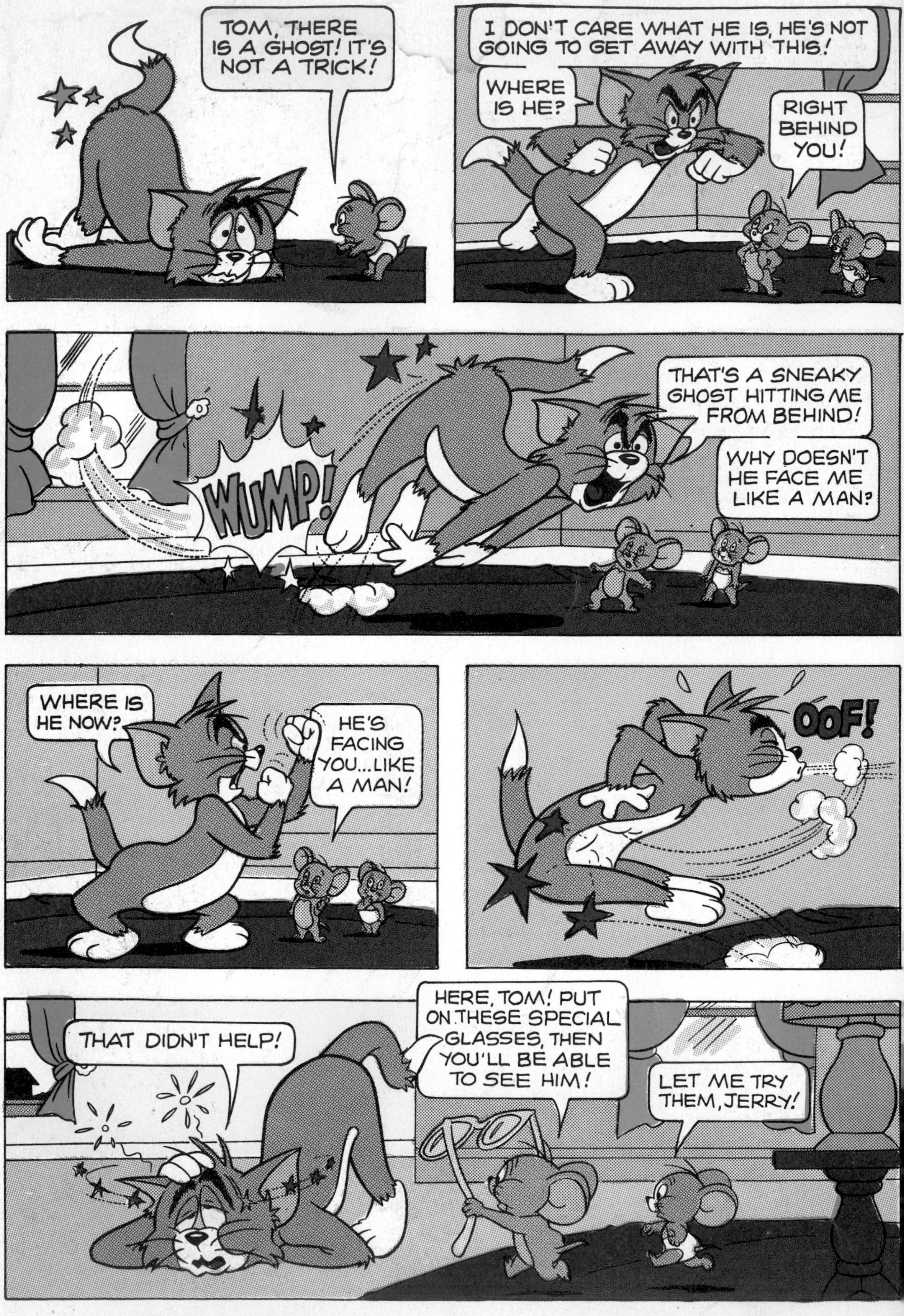
TOM, THERE IS A GHOST! IT'S NOT A TRICK!
I DON'T CARE WHAT HE IS, HE'S NOT GOING TO GET AWAY WITH THIS!
WHERE IS HE?
RIGHT BEHIND YOU!
WUMP!
THAT'S A SNEAKY GHOST HITTING ME FROM BEHIND!
WHY DOESN'T HE FACE ME LIKE A MAN?
WHERE IS HE NOW?
HE'S FACING YOU...LIKE A MAN!
OOF!
THAT DIDN'T HELP!
HERE, TOM! PUT ON THESE SPECIAL GLASSES, THEN YOU'LL BE ABLE TO SEE HIM!
LET ME TRY THEM, JERRY!